EMPIRE GARDENS

I AM
A RAINDROP

NOTE TO ADULTS

WHO AM I is a series of ten books centered around themes from the world of Nature, with an emphasis on Ecology. The very imaginative illustrations and simple texts are designed to enrich the child's understanding of the natural and social environment. Reading at this level can be made even more enjoyable if it is accompanied by a dialogue between the child and an adult, such as a parent or teacher.

I AM UP HERE
because this book is not
about boats or winds

or clouds,
but about what is inside the clouds
and inside the seas...
and inside the rivers...
and inside the lakes...
and inside glasses...

This book is about raindrops.

I, for example, was living in a cloud.

I was traveling and seeing different places.
From the sky I could say hello to my friends in the seas,
in the rivers and in the lakes. It was a happy life...

until it began to get cold.

The cloud began to get dark and we, the drops of water, turned into RAIN.

Other drops became
little hail stones,

or snowflakes,

or they got very hard
and turned into ice,

or others behaved mysteriously and became fog.

We, the raindrops, are **extremely** important

because we help
to bring plants into the world.

After becoming rain, I was filtered through the earth. A layer of hard soil stopped me.

I stayed there until I was taken out
with a bucket

and a little boy drank me.

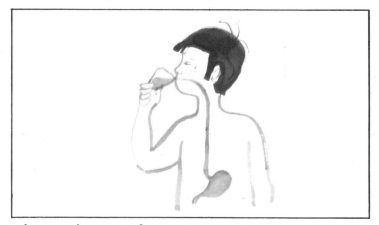

That's how I found out that boys and
girls have lots of water inside of them.

I ended up joining my raindrop
friends in a river.

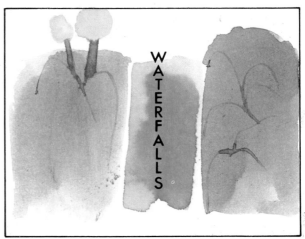

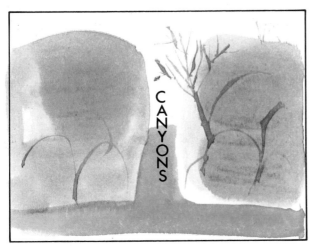

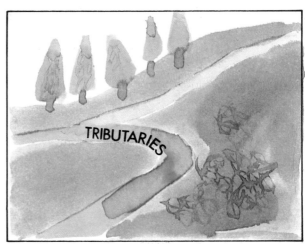

Traveling down that river I saw many
different things

and I met some very charming
and colorful people
along the river banks.

Suddenly we heard a tremendous noise:
we had arrived at a dam.

There we had no choice but to work hard
making electricity,

which is very important to people.

After going through the dam, the river continued on and we amused ourselves by babbling with each other. It seemed like nothing special was going to happen to us, but...

A CITY!

We were all terrified
and we wanted
to go back.
But it was impossible
since other drops
of water were pushing
us from behind.

We were pushed through some pipes

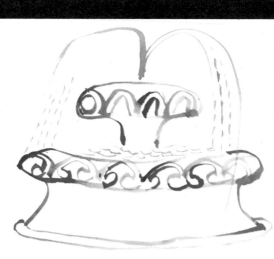

and we were used for many things.

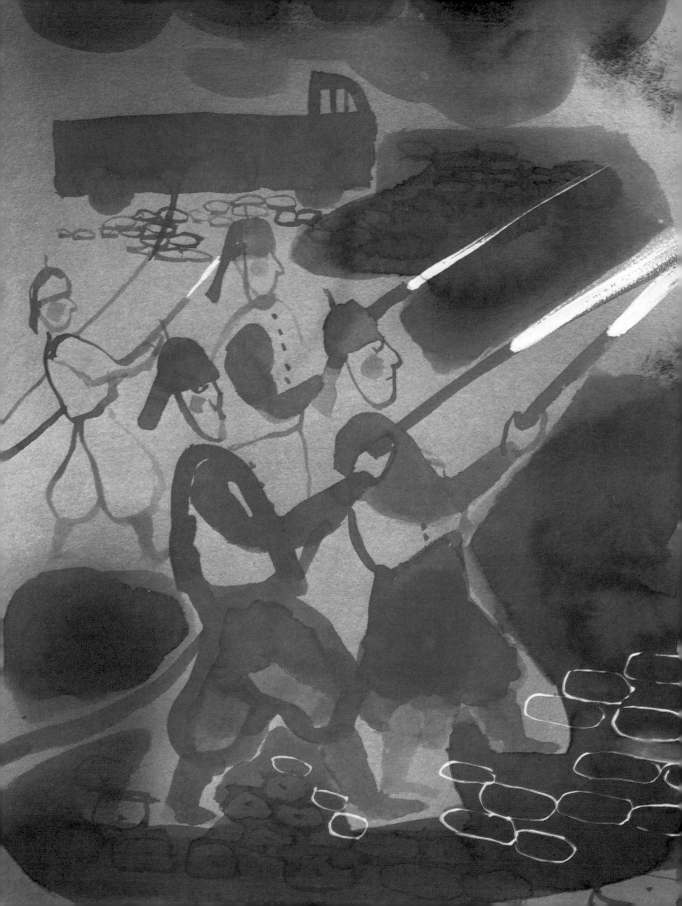

My job was to put out a fire.

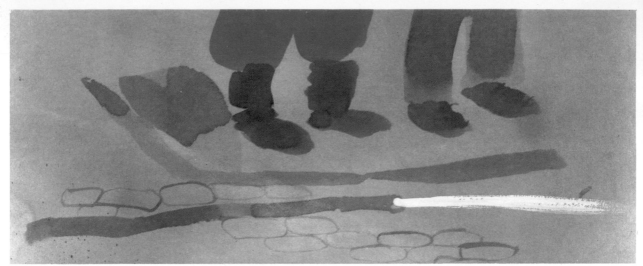

When I finished,

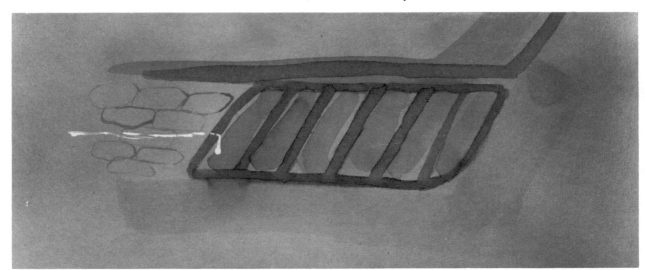

I fell through a hole.

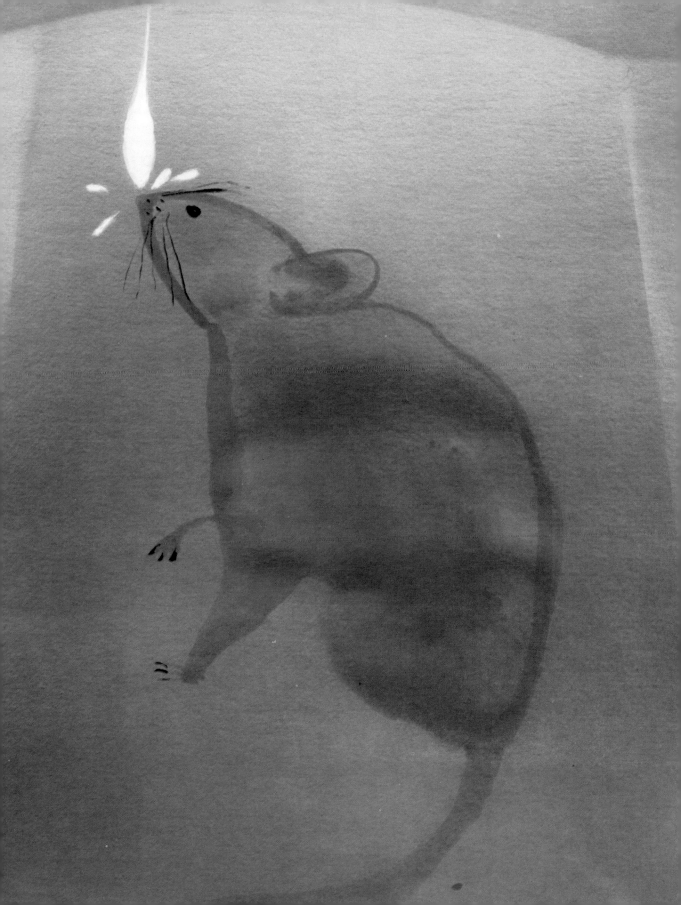

In the sewers I met a very nice young man...
he was missing a leg...
how sad.

Although he was made of tin, he gave me
confidence... he seemed courageous
and adventurous.

But I think that later on he ran into some bad luck.

When I got out into the sunlight again
I was a real mess.
There were no fish around.

THERE WERE ONLY
tomato cans
pieces of glass
torn sneakers
old tires
rotten oranges
soda bottles
candy wrappers
plastic bags
lamp shades
Cinderella's shoe...

Finally we arrived at the sea.

There, the drops of salt water couldn't understand why we were so dirty. The reason was because we had been working.

I spent some time there waiting in the sun's heat until I evaporated.

And now, once again, I am in a cloud,

although this book was not about winds, or boats or clouds, but about what there is inside the clouds... and inside the seas... and inside the lakes... and inside glasses...